Crime Scene and Evidence Photographer's Guide

Steven Staggs

Crime Scene and Evidence Photographer's Guide

by Steven Staggs

Published by:

 Staggs Publishing
P. O. Box 1565
Wildomar, CA 92595-1565 U.S.A.
http://www.staggspublishing.com

Third printing 2004
Printed in the United States of America
ISBN 0-9661970-0-3

All artwork and photography by the author, unless otherwise credited

Table of Contents

Photographing Specific Types of Crimes and Scenes 27

About the Author

Steven Staggs has been in law enforcement for 25 years and has extensive experience in crime scene photography and identification. He has testified in superior court concerning his crime scene, evidence, and autopsy photography and has handled high profile cases including a nationally publicized serial homicide case.

For the past 14 years Steve has been a forensic photography instructor and has trained more than 2,000 crime scene technicians and investigators for police and sheriffs' departments, district attorneys' offices, and federal agencies. He is also a guest speaker for investigators' associations and provides consulting to law enforcement agencies.

Steve was prompted to write this handbook in response to requests by crime scene investigators and forensic photographers who desired a practical and concise field handbook for crime scene and evidence photography.

Steve welcomes your questions and comments and can be contacted via E-Mail at:

steve@staggspublishing.com

Additional Resources

Additional information on crime scene investigations and photography can be found on the internet at the following world wide web sites:

http://www.crime-scene-investigator.net/index.html

http://www.staggspublishing.com/index.html

Introduction

From documenting a homicide scene to recording the detail of a bite mark, photographs can communicate more about crime scenes and the appearance of evidence than the written report. Photography is a valuable tool for recording the crime scene and explaining evidence to others.

This handbook is designed to be a field reference for those responsible for photography at the crime scene. It may be used by law enforcement officers, investigators, and crime scene technicians. It contains instructions for photographing a variety of crimes scenes and various types of evidence. It is a valuable reference tool when combined with training and experience.

While this handbook contains instructions for various photographic techniques, the techniques in this handbook require basic photography skills and a working knowledge of the camera and accessories used by the photographer. This handbook is not intended to prescribe policies or procedures in the area of crime scene photography or investigation. Policies and procedures are established by the investigating agencies.

It is not the purpose of this handbook to reprint all the information that is otherwise available to the author and publisher, but to complement and amplify other texts. You are urged to read all the available material, learn as much as possible about crime scene and evidence photography, and tailor the information to your individual and agency needs.

Every effort has been made to make this handbook as complete and accurate as possible. However, there may be mistakes, both typographical and in content. Therefore, this handbook should be used only as a general guide and not as the ultimate source of crime scene and evidence photography information. Furthermore, this handbook contains information on crime scene and evidence photography only up to the printing date. The author and publisher shall have neither liability nor responsibility to any person or entity with respect to any loss or damage caused, or alleged to be caused, directly or indirectly by the information contained in this handbook.

Camera and Lighting Techniques

Technical Photography

Photographs must be accurate representations of the crime scene and evidence. To be accurate representations, the photographs must be good technical photographs. Good technical photographs must be correctly exposed, have maximum depth of field, be free from distortion, and be in sharp focus.

Correct Exposure

Correct exposures are necessary for the film to capture detail in all parts of a scene, including highlight areas and shadows. Underexposed film looses detail in the shadows while overexposed film looses detail in the highlight areas.

Exposure is controlled by the shutter speed and lens aperture. Most cameras can be operated in manual and automatic modes. Automatic systems and automatic flash units produce adequate results in normal situations. However, in some situations the automatic exposure systems may produce incorrect exposures.

Some common problem lighting situations to beware of include bright, sun lighted scenes with deep shadows and back lighting. In these situations you should consider flash fill or bracketing exposures. See the camera operator's manual for information on obtaining correct exposures in different lighting situations.

Maximum Depth of Field

Depth of field is the area in a photograph where objects are in sharp focus. Crime scene and evidence photographs should have as much in focus as possible (a deep plane of sharpness).

In crime scene and evidence photography, depth of field is usually controlled by f-stop selection. The smaller the lens

opening (e.g., f/22) the greater the depth of field. The larger
the lens opening (e.g., f/1.8) the smaller the depth of field.

Shallow plane of focus — f/1.8
was used for this photograph
which produced poor depth of
field.

Deep plane of focus — f/22
was used for this photograph
which produced greater depth of
field.

Other factors that effect depth of field include the focal length
of the lens and the distance from camera to subject. Long focal
length lenses (e.g., 135mm) produce shallow planes of sharpness while short focal length lenses (e.g., 28mm) produce deep
planes of sharpness. Short camera to subject distances produce shallower planes of focus than longer camera to subject
distances.

You can anticipate the depth of field by checking the depth of
field scale engraved on most lenses (see illustration on the
next page).

Free from Distortion

Technical photographs must be as free from distortion as possible and must have good perspective. To accomplish this:

• Use a normal focal length lens when ever possible (a 50mm
  lens is considered the normal lens for a 35mm camera).
  Long focal length lenses give a telephoto effect, and short
  focal length lenses produce wide-angle distortion.

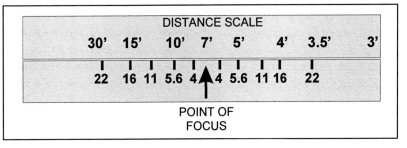

Using the Depth of Field Scale Engraved on Most Lenses — In this example the focus is set for a 7 foot distance. The depth of field scale indicates that if f/16 were in use objects from 15 feet to 4 feet would be in focus (a deep plane of focus). If f/5.6 were in use, objects from 10 feet to 5 feet would be in sharp focus (a shallow plane of focus).

• Keep the camera as level as possible.

• Hold the camera at eye level (between 4.5 and 6 feet above the ground) whenever possible.

Sharp Focus

Technical photographs must be in sharp focus. To accomplish this:

• Keep the camera steady (use a tripod if the shutter speed is less then 1/60 second).

• Focus carefully.

• Use maximum depth of field.

Flash Illumination

Types of Flash Illumination

Manual flash—When you use a manual flash, set the lens f/stop for the flash-to-subject distance.

Automatic flash—Automatic flash units use distance ranges. Each range has a minimum and maximum distance. An f/stop is assigned to each range. Changing to a new range requires a change in f/stop. Never work an automatic flash at its maximum range, especially in less than ideal conditions.

When in automatic flash, make sure the camera shutter speed dial is set to the flash synchronization speed. When photographing a high key scene (light or reflective background) bracket by opening up one or two f/stops. Overexposure is not as bad as under exposure; overexposed negatives can be printed better than underexposed negatives.

Dedicated flash—The basic dedicated flash unit sets the correct flash synchronization speed when the flash is in operation. It uses an automatic sensor and distance ranges. You must set the appropriate f/stop for the distance range. More advanced dedicated flash units may set both the correct flash synchronization speed and f/stop for the automatic range selected. It may also have a "ready light" in viewfinder.

Dedicated TTL Flash — The dedicated TTL (through-the-lens) flash uses a sensor inside the camera to control the duration of the flash. Use smaller f/stops for short distances and larger f/stops for long distances. A "confidence light" or a "warning light" will indicate whether a useable f/stop was selected. If the equipment indicates there was not enough light, select a larger lens aperture and rephotograph the photograph. Dedicated TTL flash units can usually be used in manual and automatic modes, as well as TTL. For exposure compensation with dedicated TTL units, use the exposure compensation dial.

Problems with electronic flash

Distances—Light produced by an electronic flash falls off quickly. This effect is the inverse square law of light (if the distance between the flash and subject is doubled, the illumination will drop to one quarter of the original) and results in bright foregrounds and dark backgrounds.

This can be a problem with flash photographs outdoors at night. It may be necessary to use an automatic flash distance range that is twice the actual flash-to-subject distance or use manual flash settings (open up 2 f/stops). Other solutions include using a different lighting technique such as multiple flash, painting with light, or available light (existing light without electronic flash).

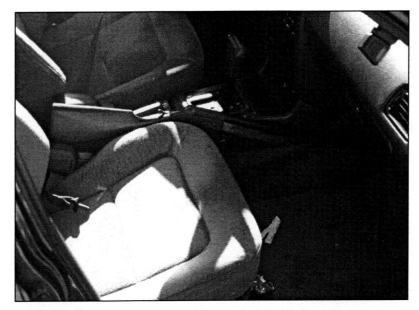

Photographing into a vehicle with existing light — exposures with strong sunlight entering a vehicle compartment usually result in photographs with deep shadows. Detail in the deep shadow areas may not be recorded on the film.

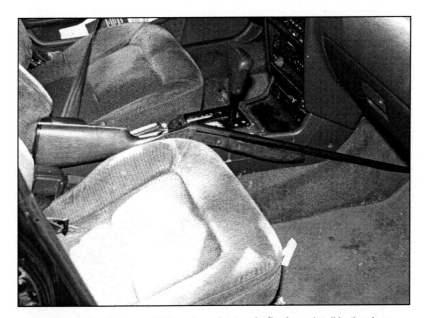

Photographing into a vehicle using electronic flash — detail in the deep shadow areas is recorded. Electronic flash is also useful for photographing into vehicle trunks and engine compartments.

Reflective Surfaces—Automatic flash units can shut off too soon due to reflected light from surfaces such as tile, white walls, or chrome. To avoid an underexposed photograph you may bracket to larger lens openings, diffuse the flash, angle the flash, or use manual flash.

Bounce Flash

Use bounce lighting for less contrast, softer lighting, intensity control, or increased angle of coverage.

Technique—Angle the flash to reflect off a white or light colored surface. With manual flash add the distance up and down for the flash-to-subject distance, then add in the absorbence loss (one to three f/stops). With automatic flash with the sensor facing the subject, use a range for two or more times the actual flash-to-subject distance.

Multiple Flash

To illuminate large areas you can get good results using several flash units positioned around the scene. The flash units can be triggered simultaneously by connecting them with sync cords or using photocell devices that remotely trigger the flash units when the camera mounted flash fires. To balance the intensity of each of the flash units, distance the flash units from the subject to provide the same f/stop for each flash.

Flash Fill

When to Use Flash Fill

In scenes illuminated by bright sunlight there will usually be dark shadow areas. Detail in the deep shadow areas will be lost when the exposure is based on the overall brightness of the scene. With the use of flash fill, the brightness level in the shadow areas can be raised to the overall brightness of the scene.

Without flash fill — detail in
shadow areas is lost.

With flash fill — detail in the
shadow areas is recorded.

Technique

1. Set the shutter speed to the camera's flash synchronization speed (usually 1/60 or 1/125 second).

2. Use the camera's light meter to determine the correct f/stop for the shutter speed selected. Set that f/stop on your lens.

3. With the flash on manual, find the flash-to-subject distance for the f/stop that was selected.

4. Position the flash unit at that distance from the shadow area and take the photograph.

You may wish to use a flash remote cord so you can have more flexibility in choosing the proper angle for the fill flash.

Cameras with dedicated TTL flash systems can provide automatic flash fill. Consult the equipment instruction manual for further instructions.

Painting With Light

When to Use Painting With Light

Painting with light is especially useful for large crime scenes at night when a single flash will not provide adequate coverage. Painting with light is frequently used at night traffic collision scenes to provide lighting for large areas.

Single electronic flash - does not provide adequate coverage   **With painting with light —** area of coverage is increased

Technique

The shutter is left open while a light source is moved around until all of the scene is properly illuminated. The light source can be a flashlight, spotlight, etc. The most effective light source is an electronic flash unit with a "test fire" button.

1. Mount the camera on a sturdy tripod.

2. Equip the camera with an efficient lens shade.

3. Screw a locking cable release into the camera shutter release.

4. Set the shutter speed dial to B (bulb).

5. Determine the f-stop based on the *flash-to-subject* distance (not the camera to subject distance).

6. Focus carefully.

7. Depress the cable release and lock it to hold the shutter open.

8. Fire the electronic flash, by pressing the "test fire" button, to light areas of the scene. The number of flashes and angle of the flashes will depend on the size and character of the scene. Do not point the flash directly at the camera and keep yourself out of the view of the camera.

9. Unlock the cable release and allow the shutter to close.

10. Advance the film.

Note: If there will be vehicle traffic through the scene during the painting with light exposure, the streaking of headlights and taillights will record in the photograph. In such situations you may wish to cover the camera lens between flashes to block out ambient light.

Available Light Photography

When to Use Available Light Photography

Available light photography is especially useful for large crime scenes at night when a single flash will not provide adequate coverage and when there is some ambient lighting present. Lighting may be from street lamps, parking lot lamps, or even moonlight. Available light from street lamps is frequently used at night traffic collision scenes to provide lighting for large areas.

Techniques

You may be able to get an adequate light meter reading to operate your camera in manual settings. Automatic cameras may also operate in low-light conditions. Many supplementary light meters provide accurate readings in very low-light conditions.

Using the available light for a nighttime exposure — the area of coverage is normally greater than lighting from a single electronic flash.

When obtaining a light meter reading do not point the light meter directly at lights in your scene, or the photograph will be underexposed. Since lighting is usually contrasty at night (light sources are many times brighter than shadow areas), determine which area of the scene is most important and aim the light meter in that area.

Use a tripod and cable release to avoid camera movement during the exposure. Bracketing exposures will help to insure a good photograph.

Photographing Crime Scenes

Steps in Photographing the Crime Scene

Once the crime scene has been secured and preliminary notes have been taken, photography should begin. A complete set of overview photographs should be taken as soon as possible. The overview photographs should be followed with photographs of the evidence before it is collected.

Walk Through

Prior to photographing the crime scene, the photographer should discuss the crime, evidence and photographs needed with other investigators at the scene. The photographer and an investigator should walk through the scene and decide what must be photographed.

The Three Step Approach

When photographically documenting a crime scene, it is usually best to use a three step approach:

1. Show the overall scene with *overview photographs*

2. Show the location of evidence with *mid-range photos*

3. Show the details of evidence with *close-up photoraphs*

Using this three step approach, working from the outside of the scene in to the smallest items of evidence, will normally provide a complete photographic documentation of the crime scene and its related evidence.

Overview Photographs

The purpose of overview photographs is to enable others to visualize the scene as you, the photographer, first saw it. Plan your photographs with this in mind. Take at least one complete set of photographs before the scene is altered or disturbed. If something was moved before you arrived, do not try to reconstruct the scene before the photography. The photographs should show the scene as *you* found it.

Do not let investigators or crime scene equipment appear in the photographs. Be careful not to destroy any evidence while taking the photographs.

Outside the Scene

In cases involving crime scenes located within buildings, begin the overview photographs with the exterior of the building. In some cases you may need to photograph a large portion of the surrounding area, such as vehicles parked on streets or in parking lots, alleys, or escape routes. One of the exterior overview photographs should include an identifying landmark such as a street sign or address plaque. Aerial photographs of the scene and the surrounding area can be useful in some types of cases. The series of exterior photographs should normally include all doors, windows, and other means of entrance or exit to and from the building.

Inside the Scene

Plan your interior overview photographs to show how things would appear to anyone walking through the scene. For each room or area:

1. Begin with a view of the entrance.

2. Photograph the room or area as it appears when you first step inside.

3. Take overview photographs from each corner of the room to show the layout of the room. A wide angle lens is usually used for interior overview photographs. In large rooms you may need to take additional photographs from other locations for complete coverage.

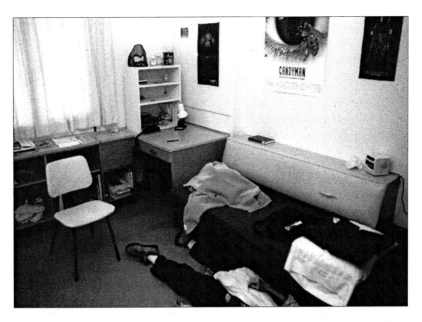

Overview photograph 1 — taken from the first corner of the room

Overview photograph 2 — moving clockwise, taken from second corner of room

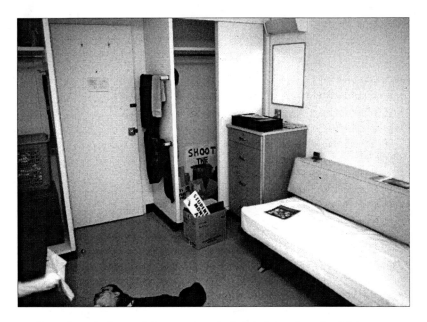

Overview photograph 3 — moving clockwise, taken from the third corner of room

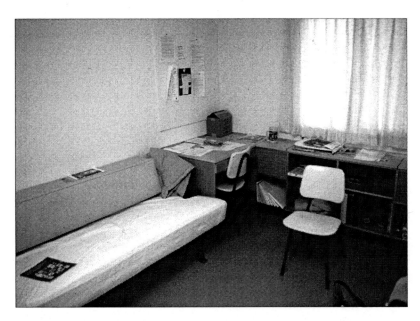

Overview photograph 4 — moving clockwise, taken from the last corner of the room

These overview photographs, along with mid-range photographs, should also show the positions of any potential items of evidence. If the overview photographs do not show the location of a specific item of evidence, take a mid-range photograph or an additional overview photograph from another angle to show the location of the evidence.

4. Continue with photographs of other rooms connected with the crime scene. If the crime scene is an apartment, hotel, or office, you may also want to take photographs of hallways, stairwells and similar areas.

Mid-Range Photographs

Mid-range photographs further establish the location of evidence and the relationship of evidence and items in the crime scene. See *Photographing Specific Crime Scenes,* and *Photographing Evidence,* for more information on mid-range photographs.

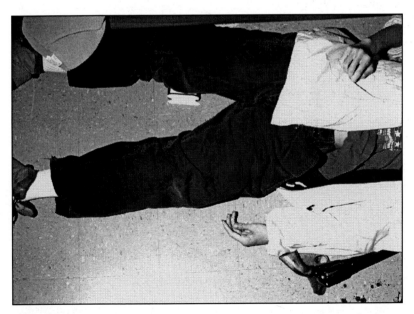

Mid-range photograph — taken to establish the location of evidence in the crime scene

Close-Up Photographs

Close-up photographs are used to show the details of evidence at the crime scene. See *Photographing Evidence*, for more information on close-up photography.

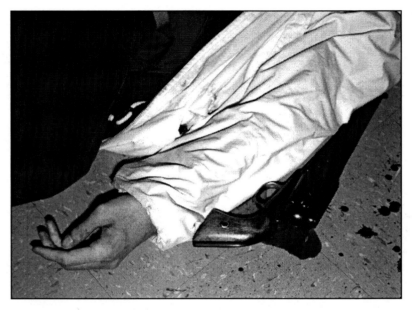

Close-up photograph — shows the details of evidence

Using Video to Record the Crime Scene

Video taping is valuable for showing an overview of the crime scene and should be used in major cases. Video taping provides an easily understandable viewing medium that shows the layout of crime scene and the location of evidence.

Techniques for Crime Scene Video Taping

When video taping crime, scenes follow these steps:

1. Start the video tape with a brief introduction presented by an investigator. The introduction should include the date, time, location, type of crime scene, and any other

important introductory information. The introduction should also include a brief description of the rooms and evidence will be viewed in the video tape. The investigator may want to use a basic diagram as an illustration during the introduction.

2. Video tape the crime scene, after the introduction, without any audio recording.

3. Begin video taping the crime scene with a general overview of the scene and surrounding area.

4. Continue throughout the scene using wide angle and close up views to show the layout of the scene, location of evidence, and the relevance of evidence within the crime scene.

5. While video taping, use slow camera movements such as panning, and zooming.

Records of Photographs

Notes should be taken to identify what photographs were taken and/or what each photograph was intended to show or accomplish. This record will assist the photographer in remembering what he/she was trying to demonstrate with each photograph. It will also assist others who view the photographs at a later time. It is recommended a form, such as the one on the next page, be used at the time the photographs are taken.

PHOTOGRAPHIC REPORT	Case Number:	Scene No.
	Film Roll No.	Page:

Date:	Location		

Make and model camera, lens:

Film type and ISO:	Light source:		

	Description of photograph	Lens, light source (if different from above), filter, etc.	Date	Time
1				
2				
3				
4				
5				
6				
7				
8				
9				
10				
11				
12				
13				
14				
15				
16				
17				
18				
19				
20				
21				
22				
23				
24				

Photographer:	Approved:	Date:

Photographing Specific Types of Crimes and Scenes

Note: Each crime scene has unique characteristics. The type of photographs needed for complete documentation will be determined at the scene by the investigators familiar with the crime. While the following are some of the common types of photographs taken at certain scenes, they should not be considered comprehensive lists of all the photographs needed in every case.

Be sure to discuss the photography with the investigators familiar with the crime. The investigators can point out things that may not appear important but should be photographed.

Homicide

When photographing a homicide, take a series of photographs that will help other investigators, the District Attorney and perhaps a jury understand where and how the crime was committed. These photographs can be used to recreate the crime and to prove or disprove a theory or a suspect's explanation.

Use color film for all but selected evidence photographs. Usually you cannot take too many photographs of a homicide.

Photographs to Consider

When photographing a homicide inside a residence photographs should include the following:

1. Exterior of the building

   All sides of the building (show address plaque)

   All doors, windows, and other means of entrance or exit

   Escape routes

   Neighborhood, street, and vehicles

   Aerial photographs in some cases

2. Evidence outside the building

   Impressions

   Forced entry

   Other evidence such as blood trails, and dropped items

3. Entrance into the scene

   Room in which the body was found

   Adjoining rooms, hallways, and stairwells

4. Body from five angles

   Head to feet

   Right side

   Feet to head

   Left side

   Overhead (straight down)

5. Close-up of body wounds

   Two photographs of each body wound — first to show location on body and second to show close-up of wound

6. Weapons

   Weapon in relation to body, if possible

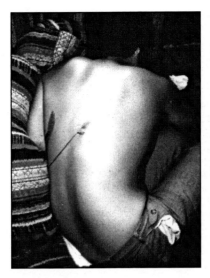 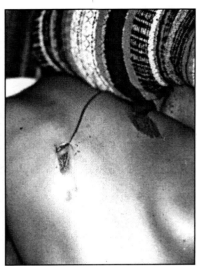

Photographs of knife wounds on a homicide victim.

Bullet holes (two photographs, one to show location and second a close-up with measuring device)

7. Trace evidence

   Blood stain

   Fingerprints

   Footprints in dust or blood

8. Signs of activity prior to the homicide

   Lights, TV, radio or appliances that are on

   Cups, glasses on table, or telephone off hook

   Cigarettes in ash tray

9. Evidence of a struggle

   Overturned furniture or broken items

   Blood stains

10. View from positions witnesses had at time of the crime—a 35mm lens will provide a good representation of a person's view

11. Area under the body after it is moved

12. Portions of the scene after the body has been removed

Suicide

If there is any doubt that the death is a suicide, photograph the scene as a homicide.

Photographs of a Known Suicide

Hanging

1. Knots, how and to what the rope was fastened
2. Injury to neck
3. Doors and windows locked from inside
4. Kicked over chair
5. Suicide note

Gunshot Suicide

1. Position of weapon in relation to body
2. Position of body

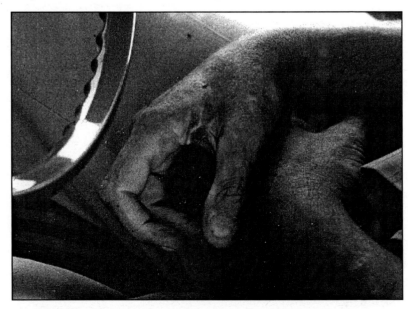

Photograph gunshot residue on the hands of suicide victims. Note on the victim's hand the pattern of the hammer from the revolver used in the suicide.

3. Wound (entrance and exit)

4. Soot or tattooing at entrance wound

5. Gunshot residue on hands

6. Locked doors

7. Suicide note

Dead Body Cases

Drowning

In a drowning case the body is the main point of interest. It is necessary to determine whether the victim actually died by drowning or was thrown into the water after death from another cause.

1. Photograph the entire body. Photograph at five angles and from the sides at ground level.

2. Photograph close-ups of mouth (open or closed), wounds, markings, bruises, discoloration, articles (such as seaweed) grasped in hand, and any rope or wire bindings.

Autopsy Photography

Most photographs at an autopsy are taken under the direction of the pathologist. In many jurisdictions the coroner's office will take the photographs. Always use color film for autopsy photography.

Suggested Photographs

• Overall photographs of the body before the body is unclothed or cleaned up

• Overall photographs of the body after the body is unclothed

• Close-ups of all wounds, including defense wounds, before and after clean-up (include scale and number multiple wounds)

• Tattoos, marks or scars including a scale

Autopsy photograph — close-up of neck wound caused by a hammer.

- Gunshot wounds, including any visible pattern of gunshot residue, with a scale
- Body after hair is shaved or wound is washed
- Victim's hands if there is any gunshot residue
- Bite marks with a scale
- Tire marks or marks from vehicle with a scale
- Injuries and trauma as directed by the pathologist

Equipment for Photographing Autopsies

- Always use color film and no filter.
- Use color charts to determine age of injury.
- Use a scale (the ABFO #2 scale is preferred for injury photography).
- Flash unit with diffused lighting, ring light or micro flash
- Macro lens, medical lens, or close-up accessory as needed

Gunshot Wounds

Equipment for Photographing Gunshot Wounds

- Film: while color film is normally used, black and white film can produce photographs with greater contrast (improved detail for showing soot and tattooing). Consider using both types of film.

- Use a scale to show size (the ABFO #2 scale is preferred).

- Flash unit with diffused lighting, ring light or micro flash.

- Macro lens, medical lens, or close-up accessory as needed.

Techniques for Photographing Gunshot Wounds

- Use orientation photographs to identify the locations of each wound on the body.

- Avoid distortion by taking close-up photographs with the film plane parallel to the wound.

- Take two photographs of each wound. One photograph without the scale and one with the scale.

- With numerous wounds, number each wound with a fine marking pen or small adhesive label.

- Position the scale on the same plane as the gunshot wound.

- Focus carefully.

- Use diffused direct flash (wide angle diffuser, handkerchief or other diffusion material placed over the electronic flash head). The most common problem is overexposure caused by too much electronic flash.

- In most cases, it is important to photograph all surfaces of the body to also indicate where there is an absence of wounds (e.g., the victim was not shot in the back).

Domestic Violence, Assaults and Injuries

When photographing injuries, be sure to show the face of victim, for identification purposes, in at least one of the photographs. Photograph old scars and fading bruises which may indicate a pattern of abuse over time. When necessary, take additional photographs 24 to 48 hours after the offense when the coloring and size of the victim's bruises become more visible.

Equipment for Photographing Assaults and Injuries

• Always use color film and no filter.

• Use color charts to determine age of injury.

• Use a scale. The ABFO #2 scale is preferred for injury photography.

• Use an electronic flash unit with diffused lighting, ring light, or micro flash

• Use a macro lens, medical lens, or close-up accessory, as needed

Visible Bruises, Bite Marks, and Other Injuries

• Take an orientation photograph.

• Take close-up photographs of each injury with the film plane parallel to the wound to avoid distortion.

• Use a scale positioned on the same plane as the bite mark.

• Use a color chart or color control patches to determine age of injuries.

• Focus carefully.

• Use a diffused direct flash (wide angle diffuser, handkerchief or other diffusion material placed over the electronic flash head). the most common problem is overexposure caused by too much electronic flash.

Ultraviolet Photography

Ultraviolet (UV) photography can produce high resolution photographs of skin surfaces. It is a good technique for photographing bite marks, cuts, and scratches. Bruises with blood accumulation close to the skin surface can also be photographed with UV photography.

Equipment

• 35mm camera.

• A lens capable of transmitting light between 300nm and 370nm. (Most lenses are designed to prevent excess UV transmission. A lens can be tested with a spectrophotometer to determine if it can transmit light between 300nm and 370nm.)

• High speed black and white film.

• UV light source (such as UV electronic flash, alternate light source, and "black light.")

• ABFO #2 scale.

• Darkroom or room without visible light.

Procedure

1. Position camera with film plane parallel to the plane of injury

2. Include a scale on same plane as the injury

3. Focus carefully

4. Darken the room and use an UV light source

5. With the light meter reading as a starting point, bracket exposures

Photograph the point of entry with overview and close-up views.

Property Crime

Residential and Commercial Burglary Scenes

Suggested Photographs

1. Exterior of building

2. Evidence outside building (such as footprints and tire tracks)

3. Point of entry (orientation and close-ups)

4. Entrance into scene

5. Interior views (overview photographs of rooms; mid-range and close-up photographs of evidence)

6. Area from which articles were removed

7. Damage to locks, safe, doors, and tool marks (orientation and close-ups)

8. Articles or tools left at the scene by the suspect

9. Trace evidence (such as burned matches, cigarette butts, and blood)

10. Other physical evidence (such as fingerprints before they are lifted and footprints in dust on floors)

Vehicle Burglary Scenes

Suggested Photographs

1. Overview photographs of scene and vehicle
2. Evidence outside vehicle (such as footprints and tire tracks)
3. Point of entry (orientation and close-ups)
4. Interior views (overview photographs, mid-range and close up photographs of evidence)
5. Area from which valuable articles were removed
6. Tool marks, damage to vehicle (orientation and close-ups)
7. Articles or tools left at the scene by the suspect
8. Trace evidence (such as burned matches, cigarette butts, and blood)
9. Other physical evidence (such as fingerprints before they are lifted)

Arson and Fire Scene

Buildings

Exterior of Building

1. All sides of the building to show the extent of fire damage and the locations of doors and windows
2. Fuse boxes, gas meters, and chimneys
3. Evidence including foot and tire impressions, and explosion debris
4. Evidence of forced entry
5. Heat and burn patterns on exterior window frames, doors, walls and roof
6. Smoke and heat patterns above windows and doors (both sides of exterior doors)

7. Overhead shot (if possible) from ladder, nearby building, or aircraft

8. Bystanders and parked vehicles

Interior of Building

Photograph the scene in a logical sequence. Consider photographing from areas of least damage to areas of most damage.

1. All rooms and areas inside building

2. Walls, ceilings, and doorways

3. Both sides of interior doors

4. Area of fire origin—before any excavation—showing floor, ceiling, and nearby walls

5. Evidence found during excavation

6. Burn patterns at doorways to indicate the spread of fire between rooms

7. Burn patterns on walls show the direction of the spread of the fire

8. Furniture and inventory

Burn patterns often show the direction of the spread of the fire.

Vehicles

The vehicle should be photographed at the fire scene. Surrounding areas should also be photographed. If the vehicle has been taken to a wrecking yard, then the original scene should be examined for evidence and photographed.

Photographs of the vehicle may include:

1. Four sides of vehicle

2. Four sides of vehicle with hood, trunk and all doors standing open

3. Engine compartment

4. Trunk

5. Passenger compartment

6. Door hinges and window glass to show status of doors and windows at the time of the fire

7. Evidence of forced entry or vehicle theft

Vehicle arson photographs include exterior views of the vehicle.

Interior views of the vehicle may show burn patterns and indicate the fire origin.

Fire Victims

If dead, photograph the scene as you would a homicide (see *Photographing Homicides*)

If alive, photograph the scene as you would for injuries (see *Photographing Injuries*)

Traffic Collisions

Take traffic collision photographs as soon as possible, before the scene can change. Show the relationship between objects in the scene. It may be a good idea to show camera locations on the field sketch.

Photographs at the Accident Scene

1. Show where the vehicles came to rest and in what position. Show the relationship of each vehicle with each other. Include some permanent, recognizable landmark in the photograph.

2. Photograph debris or marks on the roadway (such as tire marks and gouges)

3. Photograph skid marks. Take one photograph the direction of the mark to show the direction the vehicle was traveling. Take another photograph from the side to show the length of the skid mark. Photograph for the greatest depth of field possible. Photograph the contact patch on the tire and the top of the skid mark to show tire tread type. Use a polarizing filter to cut any reflection on the roadway surface.

4. Show the view each driver had approaching the key point of the accident. Show any view obstructions. Photograph from inside the vehicle. A 35mm lens will provide a good representation of a person's view.

5. Photograph the view from the point a witness observed the accident, at witness' eye level. A 35mm lens will provide a good representation of a person's view.

6. Photograph evidence to identify hit and run vehicles. Photograph paint transfer, height of damage, pieces of suspect vehicle left at scene, tire impressions, and blood.

7. Photograph the interior of any vehicle in an injury or fatal accident. Show anything in the interior that indicates body contact. Use an electronic flash when photographing the interior of a vehicle.

Use an electronic flash when photographing the interior of a vehicle.

Night Photography

Use multiple flash, painting with light, or available light for large scenes, extra long skid marks, or to show two vehicles some distance apart.

Painting with light — This large scene was photographed at night using "painting with light" to provide even lighting throughout the view.
Photograph courtesy of the Huntington Beach (CA) Police Department.

Technical Photographs of Damage to a Vehicle

Vehicle damage is photographed to help reconstruct the accident. Reconstruction can determine how one vehicle fitted against another vehicle or fixed object, from what direction the major force came, whether the vehicle rolled over, or whether it had more than one collision during the accident.

- Take vehicle damage photographs at the scene before the vehicles are moved so they will show no additional damage due to removal operations.

- Take six photographs. Two from each side in line with the axles. Take one of each end of the vehicle, straight on. If possible, take one more from overhead. (Do not take any oblique or corner photographs to show damage because the photograph will not be aligned with the axis of the vehicle. Oblique photographs conceal the amount and direction of the damage.

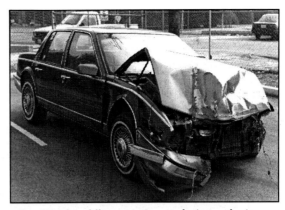

Do not take oblique or corner photographs to show vehicle damage. Oblique photographs conceal the amount and direction of the damage. Compare the appearance of the damage in the photograph above with the two photographs below.

• Use scales to indicate height and size of damage in the photographs. (See examples on the next page.)

• Always use electronic flash to fill in shadows within the damage. (See examples on the next page.)

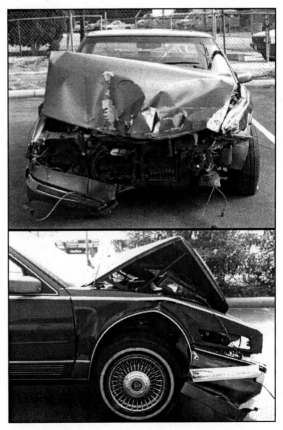

Photograph vehicle damage in line with the axis of the vehicle.

Collision damage photographed with normal lighting — shadows conceal the extent of the damage.

Collision damage photographed with electronic flash — shadows are filled in with lighting to reveal the extent of the damage.

Photographing Evidence

General Principles

Number of Photographs

Always take at least two photographs of each item of evidence. One photograph should be a mid-range view to show how the item is related to its surroundings. The second photograph should be a close up to bring out the details of the object itself.

You may be able to show several items of evidence in one mid-range photograph.

Pointing with the Camera

You can show the location of an item of evidence with a series of photographs. Begin with an overview photograph that shows the general area. In this photograph there should be a recognizable landmark. Then take a series of photographs that lead the viewer to the location of the evidence.

Using Measuring and Marking Devices

Take two photographs if a marking or measuring device is used. This is done so it can't be suggested that the scene was altered or that the device was concealing anything important.

First take a photograph of the evidence without the measuring or marking device. Then photograph the evidence with the measuring or marking device.

Always use a measuring or marking device that cannot be mistaken for evidence. Marking devices (such as numbers and identification cards) should be used only when necessary.

Close up photography

Equipment

Lenses and Close-up Devices

To record fine detail when photographing evidence, the item should fill the frame of the viewfinder. Most normal lenses will not focus close enough to be effective when photographing small items of evidence. A macro lens or some type of close-up accessory will be needed in such cases. Close-up accessories include 1:1 adapters, extension rings, bellows, reversing rings, and close-up filters.

When using more than one close-up filter (stacking filters) on the camera lens, the filters should be placed on the lens in descending order. For example, when using a +1 and a +2 filter, place the +2 on the camera lens first, followed by the +1.

Scales and Measuring Devices

Scales and measuring devices are used in crime scene and evidence photographs for three reasons:

• To orient the viewer of the photograph to the relative size of the object in the photograph

• To serve as a basis for making measurements in the photograph

• To serve as a basis for making enlargements to a specified magnification level, such as life size (1:1)

Techniques

Alignment

1. Position the scale on the same plane as the evidence.

2. Position the camera with the film plane parallel to the plane of the evidence.

Close-up Equipment — clockwise from top left: bellows, macro lens, reversing ring, close-up filters

Lighting

- Position the camera and examine the image in the view-finder. If the existing lighting provides adequate results you may be able to take the photograph with the existing light.

- If existing lighting does not provide the desired results, pre-view the photograph by moving a lighting source, such as a flashlight, around at different angles while looking in the camera's viewfinder. When the best angle of light for the evidence is observed, place the electronic flash, or other light source, in that position for the photograph.

- Beware of overexposure from too much electronic flash. Use diffused flash (wide angle diffuser, handkerchief or other diffusion material placed over the electronic flash head) or position the flash further away from the subject to avoid overexposure.

- Other lighting devices may be effective for certain types of evidence. They include micro flash (two small flashes on adjustable arms), ring lights, and copy stand lighting.

Exposure

One of the following exposure methods will normally be used when doing close up photography. In many cases, bracketing should also be considered.

• Available light exposures can be metered with the camera's internal light meter. Metering off a 18% gray card will give good results.

• TTL electronic flash exposures will be controlled by the camera's TTL flash metering system.

• Normal electronic flash exposures can be done in either automatic or manual flash.

Focusing (while hand-holding the camera)

1. Rough size (scale) the subject by focusing with the lens focus ring. Then stop focusing with the focus ring.

2. Fine focus the subject by moving the camera in and out from the subject.

3. While maintaining the fine focus by moving the camera in and out slightly, lightly depress the shutter button.

Lighting methods for copy and evidence close up photography

The following lighting methods are effective for photographing various evidence subjects. The effects should be previewed in order to select the best lighting technique for the evidence subject.

Direct Lighting

Direct lighting uses normal copy lighting with one or more light sources positioned at 45-degree angles.

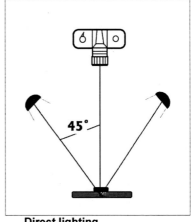

Direct lighting

Direct Reflective Lighting

Light is reflected directly off the subject into the lens. Place the subject at a 10-degree angle from the lens to film plane and place the light source at 10-degree angle from the subject. The light source reflects at a 20-degree angle into the lens. The light source may need to be diffused to prevent hot spots. This method creates very high contrast.

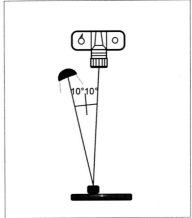

Direct reflective lighting

Oblique Lighting

Oblique lighting uses a light source at a low angle, usually to show detail by creating shadows in the subject surface. It is commonly used when photographing impressions, tool marks and certain types of fingerprints.

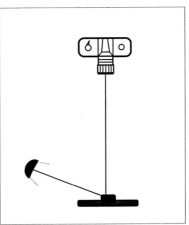

Oblique lighting

Bounce Lighting

Light is bounced off a white or reflective surface. The bounce surface may be positioned at different locations (above or to one side of the subject) to create the desired effect. This usually produces even non-glare lighting with low contrast.

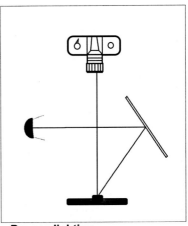

Bounce lighting

Diffused Lighting

An opaque material is placed between the light source and the the subject to diffuse the light. This usually results in even lighting with reduced reflections and hot spots.

Diffused lighting

Transmitted Lighting

With transparent subjects the light source is transmitted through the subject toward the lens. The angle of the transmitted lighting is adjusted from 90 degrees to 45 degrees for the desired effect.

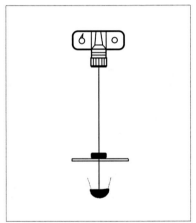

Transmitted lighting

Front Directional or Axis Lighting

A clear piece of glass is placed between the subject and lens at a 45-degree angle. The light source is positioned parallel to the film place and 45-degrees to the glass. While the light is transmitted through the glass, some is reflected downward directly on the subject. This technique is effective when photographing fingerprints on mirrors and into glasses or cups.

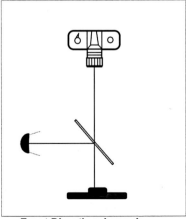

Front Directional or axis lighting

Impressions

Prior to casting an impression, such as a footprint or tire track, always photograph the impression. Casting of impressions is not always needed for later positive identification if the impression is properly photographed.

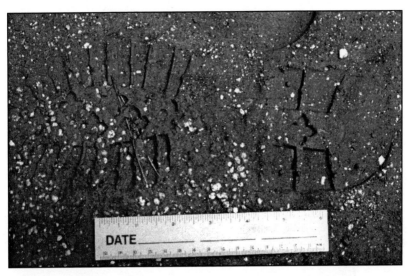

Photographing impressions — use a scale on the same plane as the impression. Keep the film plane parallel to the plane of the impression. Position the electronic flash or light source at angles that highlight the detail in the impression. Preview the photograph by using a strong light source at different angles.

Procedure

1. **Orientation Photograph:** Take a mid-range photograph to show where the impression is located in the crime scene.

2. **Close-up Photograph:** Take a close-up photograph to show detail. Use a scale on the same plane as the impression. Press the scale into the surface until it is the same depth as the impression. Keep the film plane parallel to the plane of the impression.

3. **Lighting:** Existing shadowing from daylight does not always provide the best results. Preview the photograph by looking at lighting from other angles. To do this, block out ambient light with a large piece of cardboard and use a

strong light source at different angles to find the light angles that show the best detail in the impression. Then position the electronic flash or light source at those angles for the photographs.

Another lighting technique would be to take a series of photographs with the electronic flash or light source at at least four different angles.

Impressions in materials such as blood, grease and oil, which are visible with existing light, may be photographed with existing light or with indirect electronic flash (the flash is not pointed directly at the impression).

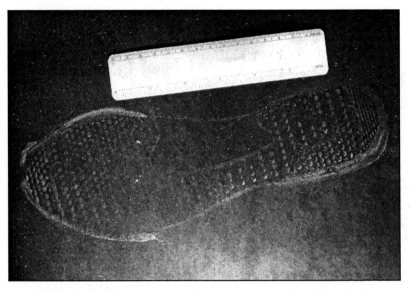

Dusty shoe print left on a vinyl chair — nearly invisible to the naked eye, this dusty shoe print was photographed using an oblique light angle. *Photograph by Joe Brown, University of California Davis Police Dept.*

4. **Tire Impressions:** Photograph tire impressions in sections showing one circumference of the tire. Do this by taking overlapping photographs with a tape measure along side the tire impression.

Fingerprints

Fingerprints should be photographed before lifting on major cases or if the latent may be destroyed when lifting. Photographs can also be used to bring out detail in a latent. Through the use of lighting, filters and processing controls, a faint latent fingerprint can be enhanced. This is done by building contrast between the latent and its background.

Equipment

1:1 cameras, copy cameras, and cameras with macro or close up lens attachments can be used to photograph fingerprints.

Films

While well-defined fingerprints can be photographed with color film, black and white film provides greater contrast and is preferred for latent print photography. The following is a list of a few black and white films that are suitable for latent fingerprint photography.

Normal contrast — Kodak T-MAX film. Develop in T-MAX developer while increasing the development time by 25% for increased contrast.

High contrast — Kodak TECHNICAL PAN 2415 film has a variable contrast range between high and low and a variable speed of ISO 25 to 320. For high contrast, expose at ISO 100 and develop in HC-110 developer.

Very high contrast — Kodak KODALITH film. Kodalith film is packaged for 35mm cameras as Kodak Ektagraphic HC Slide Film (HCS 135-36) and has an approximate ISO of 8. If developed in D-76 or HC 110 there will be a limited gray scale.

Black & white films that can be processed in color processing machines — Kodak T400 CN and Ilford XP-2 black and white films are processed in color processors. They each have an ISO of 400, are fine grain with good sharpness and resolution, and are processed in C-41 color chemistry.

Filters

Color filters, when used in black and white photography, can build contrast by either lightening or darkening the latent print or by lightening or darkening the background. To lighten a color, the color filter closest to the color is used. To darken a color, the opposite color filter is used. Refer to the charts on pages 54 and 55.

Examples

A faint powdered latent on a blue background can be enhanced with background drop-out by using a #47 blue filter. A ninhydrin developed latent on the back of U.S. currency can be enhanced in two ways with a #58 green filter. The green in the currency is lightened (background drop-out) and the violet colored ninhydrin developed latent is darkened.

Black and White Contrast Filters

Objective: To increase contrast between colors that would normally photograph as nearly the same shade of gray.

Light Information — White light is made up of a mixture of the primary colors—red, green and blue. In theory red, green, and blue light sources simultaneously projected on the same area will be white. Red and green light mixed together makes yellow. Green and blue light mixed is cyan. Blue and red light mixed is magenta.

Light Transmission Law — The filter transmits its own color (lightened in the print) and absorbs (subtracts) its complementary color (darkened in the print).

Filter Color	Filter Number	Absorbs (Darkens)	Transmits (Lightens)
Red	25A, 29	Blue & Green - Cyan	Red
Blue	47, 47B	Red & Green - Yellow	Blue
Green	58, 61	Red & Blue - Magenta	Green
Magenta	CC50M	Green	Red & Blue - Magenta
Cyan	CC50C	Red	Blue & Green - Cyan
Yellow	8, 15	Blue	Red & Green - Yellow

Selecting Black and White Films and Filters to Obtain Contrast Between Colors

Objective — To increase contrast between colors that would normally photograph as nearly the same shade of gray.

Films — Panchromatic films (T-MAX, Plus-X, etc.) are blue, green and red sensitive. Colors are shown in varying shades of gray.

Orthochromatic films (KODALITH) are blue and green sensitive only. Red will appear black in a black and white print.

Desired Photographic Result	Black and white films:	
	Panchromatic	Orthrocromatic
	Filters used to obtain result	
Blue as black	Red (25, 29)	Green (58, 61)
Blue as white	Blue (47, 47B)	Blue (47, 47B)
Blue-green as white	Cyan (50C)	Cyan (50C)
Blue-green as black	Red (25, 29)	Blue (47, 47B)
Green as white	Green (58, 61)	Green (58,61)
Green as black	Red (25,29) or blue (47,47B)	Blue (47, 47B)
Orange as black	Blue (47, 47B)	None
Orange as white	Yellow (15) or red (25, 29)	Not possible
Red as black	Blue (47, 47B)	None
Red as white	Red (25, 29)	Not possible
Violet as black	Green (58, 61)	Green (58, 61)
Violet as white	Blue (47, 47B)	Blue (47, 47B)
Yellow as black	Blue (47, 47B)	Green (58, 61)
Yellow as black	Yellow (15)	Green (58, 61)
Yellow-green as black	Blue (47, 47B)	Blue (47, 47B)
Yellow-green as white	Green (58, 61)	Green (58, 61)

NOTE: Colors of objects are hardly ever "pure." The effects described above are never perfect but the direction indicated is correct.

Without any filter – the background and fingerprint record as nearly the same shade of gray

With red filter – the red filter transmits the red background providing needed contrast

Procedures in Photographing Fingerprints

Establish the Location of the Fingerprint

Use a mid-range photograph to show where the print is located in the scene, or use the diagram and notations on the latent print card to identify the original location of the fingerprint.

Close-up Photograph

A 1:1 camera or device must be used, or a scale must be included in the photograph on the same plane as the fingerprint. Case and item numbers can be placed on the scale. Photograph the latent with the camera's film plane parallel to the fingerprint surface. Get as much depth of field as possible, especially for curved surfaces.

Exposure

Available light exposures of fingerprints with normal contrast can be metered using a gray card.

Whether using available light, electronic flash, or other illumination sources, bracketing of exposures should be considered. Bracketing may reveal more detail in "low contrast" fingerprints. Underexposing the film will separate the steps on the white end of the gray scale. Overexposure will separate the steps on the black end of the gray scale. The latitude for black and white film is generally two stops underexposure and six stops overexposure.

Photographing Specific Types of Fingerprint Subjects

Normal, dusted fingerprints with good visible detail— These surfaces can usually can be photographed without special lighting techniques.

Impressions in soft substance — Wax, putty, clay, adhesive tape, grease, or dust require the use of oblique lighting at a low angle. Preview the effect with flashlight lighting.

Porous surfaces — Surfaces such as textured wall coverings or brick, may need almost a 90-degree lighting angle to avoid the creation of shadows in the texture, which will interfere with the recording of fingerprint detail. Preview the effect with flashlight lighting.

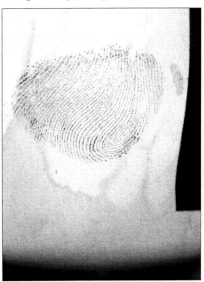

Glass — Place a white card behind the glass. Use a low oblique angle of light.

Fingerprints on glass — Use back (transmitted) lighting and a diffusion screen.

Ninhydrin developed fingerprint — Use normal black and white film with a green filter. Increase the film development time 25%.

Fingerprint on drinking glass using transmitted lighting – position a diffused light source behind the glass

Bloodstain Photography

Use color film to establish which substances in the photograph are blood stains. Black and white film records reflected light in shades of gray, so it may be difficult to determine what substances in the photography are actually blood stains. Black and white film may, however, be used for high contrast photographs or with colored filters to increase contrast between the background and blood stain. See the section on fingerprints for more information on using black and white film with colored filters.

Take orientation photographs to show locations of bloodstain evidence at the scene and close up photographs of the bloodstain to show detail.

For close up photographs, use a scale on the same plane as the bloodstain and photograph with the film plane parallel to the plane of the bloodstain. Use an oblique light angle. Very low oblique light angles, especially when dealing with fabrics, will sometimes record bloodstains best because of the difference in reflectivity between the blood and the background surface. Preview the effect with a flashlight.

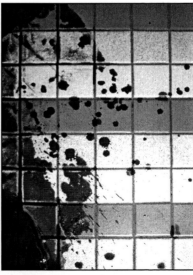

When photographing bloodstain evidence use a scale on the same plane as the bloodstain and photograph with the film plane parallel to the plane of the bloodstain. Use an oblique light angle.

Photographing Luminol

Luminol is a presumptive test for blood usually used to reveal bloodstain patterns on surfaces where the bloodstain has been cleaned or is not readily visible. Since Luminol will denature most blood enzymes after short exposure, it is important to take samples of the bloodstain for serological analysis before using Luminol.

Equipment

Camera with "B" setting, lens with f/1.8 or larger aperture, locking cable release, tripod, electronic flash, ISO 400 color print film, and timer.

Procedure

1. In darkness, spray a fine mist of a Luminol solution over the area to be searched. If luminescence is observed, note its location.

2. Turn on the room lights. Set up a camera, equipped with a locking cable release and an electronic flash, on a tripod. Take a normal photograph of the area.

3. Without moving the camera, advance the film and adjust the lens aperture to underexpose the next photograph by one or two f/stops. This can be done with an automatic camera by adjusting the exposure control setting (to a setting of −1 or −2) or with a manual camera by closing down the lens aperture (e.g. if the normal flash photograph requires a f/5.6, change the aperture to f/8 or f/11). Set the shutter speed to "B."

4. With the room darkened, open the shutter (firing the electronic flash) and lock the cable release to hold open the shutter.

5. Open the lens aperture all the way while taking care not to move the camera.

6. Lightly spray Luminol on the area in the view of the camera. Respray the area every twenty seconds to maintain luminescence. Avoid over spraying, which may cause patterns on smooth surfaces to run or may cause

background luminescence and reduce needed contrast. Close the shutter after about one minute.

7. A scale can be used to in the photograph. Attach small pieces of copper wire on the one inch marks of a ruler. The copper wire will luminesce when sprayed with Luminol.

Laser or Alternate Light Source (ALS) Photography

To photograph luminescence or florescence when using laser or alternate light sources:

1. Focus carefully.

2. Place the proper band cut off filter (red, orange, or yellow) over the lens.

3. Determine a starting exposure with the camera light meter or a separate light meter. When using a separate light meter, use the filter factor for the band cut off filter to compute the exposure.

4. Bracket by a minimum of two stops.

Injuries

When photographing injuries be sure to show the face of victim, for identification purposes, in at least one of the photographs.

Equipment for Photographing Injuries

• Always use color film and no filter.

• Use color charts to determine age of injury.

• Use a scale. The ABFO #2 scale is preferred for injury photography.

• Use an electronic flash unit with diffused lighting, ring light, or micro flash.

• Use a macro lens, medical lens, or close-up accessory as needed.

Visible Bruises, Bite Marks, and Other Injuries

- Take orientation photographs.
- Take close-up photographs with the film plane parallel to the wound to avoid distortion.
- Use a scale on the same plane as the bite mark.
- Use a color chart or color control patches to determine age of injuries.
- Focus carefully.
- Use a diffused direct flash (wide angle diffuser, handkerchief or other diffusion material placed over the electronic flash head). The most common problem is overexposure caused by too much electronic flash.

Ultraviolet Photography

Ultraviolet photography can produce high resolution photographs of skin surfaces. It is a good technique for photographing bite marks, cuts, and scratches. Bruises with blood accumulation close to the skin surface can also be photographed with UV photography.

Equipment

- 35mm camera
- A lens capable of light transmission between 300nm and 370nm. (Most lenses are designed to prevent excess UV transmission. A lens can be tested with a spectrophotometer to determine if it can transmit light between 300nm and 370nm.)
- High speed black and white film
- UV light source (such as UV electronic flash, alternate light source, or "black light").
- ABFO #2 scale
- Darkroom or room without visible light

Procedure

1. Position the camera with the film plane parallel to plane of injury.

2. Include a scale on the same plane as the injury.

3. Focus carefully.

4. Darken the room and use a UV light source.

5. With the light meter reading as a starting point, bracket exposures.

Tool Marks and Serial Numbers

Take an orientation photograph to show the location of the evidence at the scene and one or more close-up photographs to show detail.

For close up photographs, use a scale on the same plane as the evidence and photograph with the camera's film parallel to the plane of the evidence. Use an oblique light angle to create small shadows in the detail. Preview the effect with a flashlight.

Use an oblique light angle to create small shadows in the detail. Preview the effect with a flashlight.

Basic Equipment for Crime Scene Photography

Crime Scene Photography Kit

☐ Camera

☐ Normal lens (a 50mm lens is considered a normal lens for a 35mm camera)

☐ Wide angle lens (28mm or similar for a 35mm camera)

☐ Close-up lenses or accessories (e.g., macro lens, 1:1 adapter, extension tubes, bellows, reversing ring, or close up filters)

☐ Filters (red, orange, yellow, blue, and green)

☐ Electronic flash

☐ Remote sync cord for electronic flash (to operate flash when not mounted on camera)

☐ Extra camera and flash batteries

☐ Locking cable release

☐ Tripod

☐ Film (color and black and white print film)

☐ Owner's manuals for camera and flash

☐ Notebook and pen

☐ Scales (6" and 36")

☐ Gray card (to aid in getting accurate exposures)

☐ Index cards and felt pen

☐ Flashlight

Other equipment that should be considered

☐ Telephoto lenses (135mm, telephoto zoom lens for surveillance photography)

☐ Supplementary light meter for low light level readings

☐ Small tools for emergency camera repairs

☐ Blocks of wood, clothespins, and other devices for positioning evidence for close-up photography

☐ White handkerchief or other flash diffusion material

☐ Levels

☐ Tape measure

☐ Color chart or color control patches (injury photography)

☐ ABFO #2 scale (injury photography)

Photoevidence Scales

"ALPS Photoevidence Scales are a must tool for every crime scene and evidence photographer! A set should be included in every camera kit."

These unique Photoevidence Scales are used when a size or distance is to be shown in a photograph.

- Crime Scenes
- Bloodstain
- Injuries
- Horizontal and Vertical Measurements

These specially designed scales have bold black numbers on a yellow background to show up exceptionally well for both black and white and color photographs. They are even visible under ultraviolet light! Each set consists of two standard 36 inch long scales and one special scale. The standard scales have vertical numbers on one side and horizontal numbers on the flip side. The special scale has reverse horizontal numbers on one side and 36" to 72" numbering on the other side. The special scale can be combined with the standard scale, by using the connector (included), to make a six foot scale. The set of 3 flexible scales comes in a transparent plastic storage tube.

36" Flexible Plastic Scales (set of three) $ 39.95

Mini-Macro 6" Scales

Mini-macro scales are perfect for photographing small objects, scars, curved surfaces, etc. These precision scales are six inches long, flexible, matte laminated with large black numbered 1" to 6" running left to right on one side and the opposite direction on the flip side.

6" Mini-Macro Scales (set of six) $ 5.95

PhotoLog Notebooks

These pocket–sized notebooks are ideal for recording information about the photographs you take at crime scenes. Each 3½" x 5½" notebook contains 30 formatted pages, enough to record information for 360 photographs (10 rolls of 36 exposure film or 15 rolls of 24 exposure film).

PhotoLog Notebooks (set of five) $ 4.95

Other books for crime scene investigators:

Crime Scene Evidence
by Mike Byrd
© 2001   ISBN 0-9661970-5-4

Crime Scene Evidence: A Guide to the Recovery and Collection of Physical Evidence was written by a veteran crime scene investigator. The book is designed to be carried in the field and used as a reference in the recovery, collection, and packaging of crime scene evidence.

Footwear, The Missed Evidence
by Dwane S. Hilderbrand
© 1999   ISBN 0-9661970-1-1

Footwear, The Missed Evidence is a field guide to the collection and preservation of forensic footwear impression evidence. This 118 page, 5 ½" by 8 ½" publication will be your constant reference on locating, collecting and recovering footwear evidence. Whether you are at the crime scene or in the crime laboratory, you will refer to this book again and

Introduction to Fingerprint Comparison
by Gary W. Jones
© 2000   ISBN 0-9661970-3-8

Introduction to Fingerprint Comparison was written by retired FBI Supervisory Fingerprint Specialist Gary W. Jones. This 87 page 5 ½" by 8 ½" book is a valuable text in learning the basic skills in fingerprint comparison. Examples and quizzes give the reader a solid foundation on which to build comparison skills.

Courtroom Testimony
for the Fingerprint Expert

by Gary W. Jones
© 1999   ISBN 0-9661970-2-X

Courtroom Testimony for the Fingerprint Expert was written by retired FBI Supervisory Fingerprint Specialist Gary W. Jones. This 94 page 5 ½" by 8 ½" book is a valuable text in preparing to testify as an expert witness in court. You will refer to this text over and over to become more effective as an expert witness.